Traditional Natural Skin Care

Traditional
NATURAL SKIN CARE

NATASHA MOORE

WARNING

All guidelines, warnings and instructions should be read carefully *before* embarking on any of the recipes.The recipes in this book are perfectly safe when properly mixed. However, some of the ingredients may cause allergic reactions in some individuals so it is essential to do the patch-test, see page 9, before using any of the preparations in this book.

Every effort has been made to ensure that all infomation in this book is accurate. However, due to differing conditions, equipment and individual skills the publisher cannot be held responsible for any injuries, losses, or other damages which may result from the use of the information in this book.

A Siena book
Siena is an imprint of Parragon Books

First published in Great Britain in 1996 by
Parragon Book Service Ltd
Units 13-17, Avonbridge Industrial Estate
Atlantic Road, Avonmouth
Bristol BS11 9QD

ISBN 0-75251-725-2

Printed in Great Britain
Produced by Kingfisher Design Services, London

Series Editor Jenny Plucknett
Series Design Pedro Prá-Lopez, Kingfisher Design Services

Consultant Rhiannon Lewis MIFA
Editing Margaret Crowther
Illustrations Jill Moore
Typesetting/DTP Frances Prá-Lopez, Kingfisher Design Services

Contents

Making Your own Preparations

This book is an introduction to making your own, individualized skin care products using natural ingredients to gently restore and condition your skin. For centuries, beauty products have been made from natural ingredients and it is only relatively recently in our history that the preparations we put on our skin have been manufactured on a mass-produced commercial scale.

By regularly making your own skin care products you can have complete control over what goes onto your skin and ensure that what you use is as natural, fresh and as suitable for your skin type as possible. You can avoid commercial preservatives and additives present in shop-bought products that can irritate skin and you can be absolutely sure that your preparations do not cause cruelty to animals.

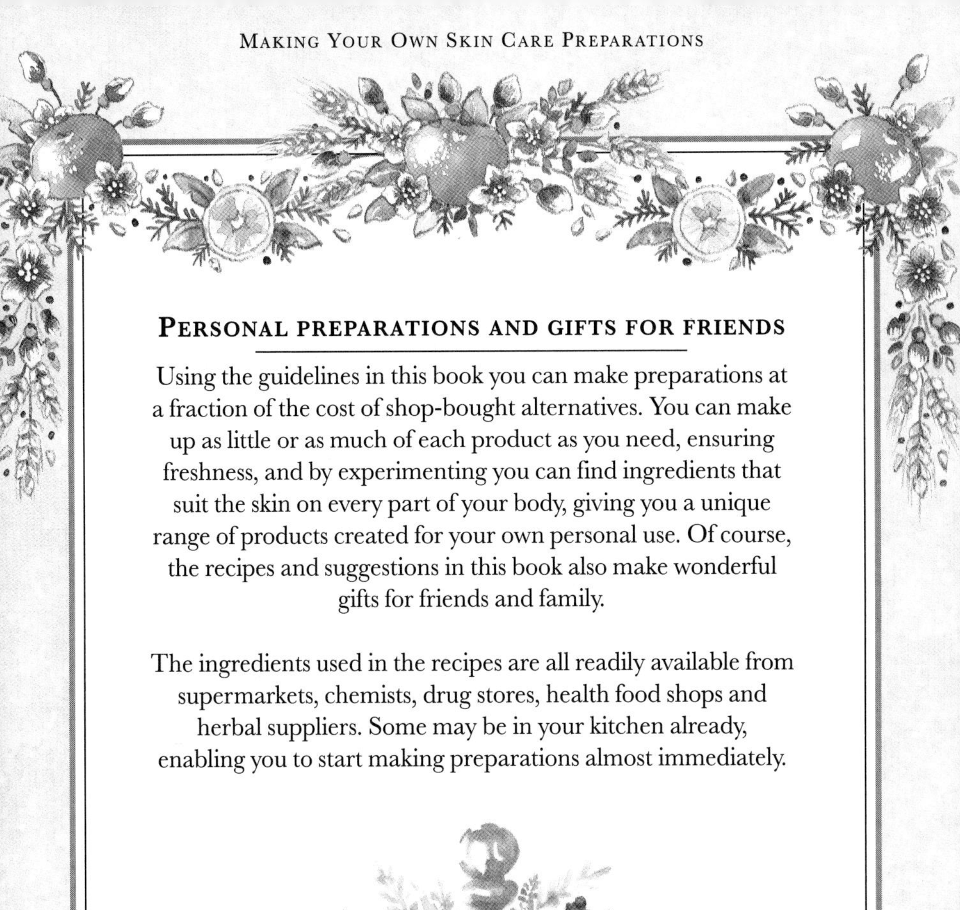

Personal preparations and gifts for friends

Using the guidelines in this book you can make preparations at a fraction of the cost of shop-bought alternatives. You can make up as little or as much of each product as you need, ensuring freshness, and by experimenting you can find ingredients that suit the skin on every part of your body, giving you a unique range of products created for your own personal use. Of course, the recipes and suggestions in this book also make wonderful gifts for friends and family.

The ingredients used in the recipes are all readily available from supermarkets, chemists, drug stores, health food shops and herbal suppliers. Some may be in your kitchen already, enabling you to start making preparations almost immediately.

You should always exercise caution when using any single ingredient or combination of ingredients on your skin for the first time. Any ingredient has the potential to irritate skin and the more sensitive your skin, the more likely it is to have an adverse reaction. The recipes in this book have been tested and are believed to be safe, but your skin is individual so it is important that you determine how it will react to what you put on it. Follow the skin test recommended below and only proceed to use a product if you have no adverse reaction to it.

Doing a Skin Test

You should not put any substance on your skin if you are allergic to it. If you do not know if your skin will be irritated by a particular ingredient, or by a combination of ingredients, carry out a patch-test first.

Substances That May Cause Irritation or Allergy

Avocado Oil • Essential Oils • Glycerine • Lanolin • Simple Tincture of Benzoin • Sweet Almond Oil • Wheatgerm Oil

WARNING

Seek medical advice first if you have any doubts about the use of any ingredients.

HOW TO CARRY OUT A PATCH-TEST

- Apply a small amount of the substance on your inner arm, immediately below the elbow. Cover with sticking plaster (unless you are allergic to plaster) and leave for 8-24 hours.
- If there is any soreness, redness or irritation, then your skin is reacting and the ingredient being tested should be avoided.

SAFETY-FIRST POINTERS

- Make sure that all the ingredients you use are fresh and pure. In most cases, if you wouldn't eat it you shouldn't put it on your skin.
- If possible, use organically produced ingredients, where appropriate. It is best not to bring pesticides or other chemicals into contact with your skin.
- Always use 100 per cent pure, unrefined (preferably cold-pressed) Vegetable and Nut Oils to ensure that they are as natural as possible.
- Maintain high standards of hygiene by ensuring that all equipment is thoroughly clean. Regularly wash your hands while involved in making preparations.
- Keeping preparations in the refrigerator will help them to last longer.

Caring for Your Skin

Pollution, air-conditioning, central heating, excessive sunshine, stress, ill-health, cigarettes and alcohol all have an adverse effect on our skin. To help counteract this, follow a wholesome diet with plenty of fresh fruit and vegetables, drink lots of water and have eight hours sleep each night. This helps to nourish the skin from inside. Developing a regular skin care routine helps to look after your skin from the outside.

HOW TO RECOGNIZE YOUR SKIN TYPE

Cleanse your face thoroughly before going to bed. On waking, before washing or cleansing your face, press one layer of a clean tissue onto your face. Hold the tissue up to the light and look for any oily, transparent areas.

If the tissue has oily marks

This indicates that you have an oily skin and could benefit from following the routine for this skin type. If the marks are present in a T-shape, relating to the position of your forehead, nose and chin, a combination skin is indicated. Usually this has an oily central panel with dry cheeks. Each area should be treated separately in your skin care routine.

If the tissue remains clean

If there are no transparent areas and your skin feels soft and supple, your skin is probably normal. But if washing with soap and water leaves your skin feeling tight and stretched, a dry skin is indicated.

SKIN CARE ROUTINES

For oily to normal skin

- **Twice-a-day** Use a light cleansing lotion or cream, followed by a skin toner/astringent and a light moisturizer. Use eye make-up remover at night.
- **Once-a-week** Use more thorough treatment such as a facial mask. Scrubs can be used twice a week.
- **Occasionally** Use a conditioning cream but always blot off any oiliness remaining after 15 minutes.

For dry to normal skin

- **Twice-a-day** Use gentle, creamy cleansers or lotions followed by a mild skin freshener/toner. It can be helpful to use a rich moisturizer daily. Use eye make-up remover at night.
- **Once-a-week** Use more intense conditioning creams and a gentle face mask.
- **Occasionally** Use mild facial scrubs. However, care should be taken if your skin is sensitive.

— 1 —

Oil and Wax Bases

The Vegetable and Nut Oils listed here, can be used as bases for skin care preparations, individually or in combination, or even mixed with other ingredients. Lanolin and Beeswax can be used to enrich and provide bulk to preparations. With these ingredients, you can create highly beneficial products to nourish, soften and restore the skin.

APRICOT OIL

- **Benefits** This moisturizes and nourishes. It can benefit most skin types, including dry, sensitive, mature and wrinkled skin. It is light and highly penetrative.
- **Uses** This oil can be used in a wide variety of face, body or bath preparations.

Avocado Oil

❊ **Benefits** This very nourishing oil can be beneficial to eyelash growth, stretch marks and most skin types, especially dry skin.

❊ **Uses** Avocado Oil can be used in baths, for cleansing, or to condition the face or body. Do not use in quantities that add up to more than 10 per cent of all ingredients.

ADDING AN OIL AS 10 PER CENT OF ALL INGREDIENTS

EXAMPLE

In a 150ml (5fl oz/⅔ cup) blend of oils, use no more than 15ml(½fl oz/ 1 tbsp) of the oil recommended for use as no more than 10 per cent of all ingredients.

Beeswax

❊ **Benefits** Softens, soothes and nourishes. Use the sun-bleached white variety which is commonly sold in solid discs. Finely grate for use.

❊ **Uses** Beeswax acts an emulsifier, helping to keep the water and oils combined in a cream, particularly when used in conjunction with Borax.

CARROT OIL

- **Benefits** This helps to rejuvenate the skin. It can be beneficial to most skin types, including dry, problem, itching, mature or wrinkled skin.
- **Uses** Carrot Oil is infused, so do not use undiluted and do not use in quantities that add up to more than 10 per cent of all ingredients, see box on page 13. It can temporarily stain the skin and clothing.

CASTOR OIL

- **Benefits** This oil is smooth, rich and suitable for most skin types. It can also be helpful to weak eyelashes and dry lips.
- **Uses** A treated version, known as Turkey Red Oil, is available. This disperses in water, making it ideal for bath oils.

COCONUT OIL

- **Benefits** A very fine, nourishing and rich oil, beneficial to the lips and hands.
- **Uses** Coconut Oil, extracted from the flesh of the coconut, is ideal for moisturizers or conditioners. Although solid when cold, it quickly melts on contact with the skin. It is also widely used in hair and scalp care.

EMULSIFYING WAX

- **Uses** This is a commercial product that can be used in skin cream recipes to bind water and oil together and stabilize them.

Grapeseed Oil

- **Benefits** This is light, easily absorbed and very versatile. It is suitable for most skin types and is ideal for body massage. Grapeseed oil is not available cold-pressed.

- **Uses** Effective on face and body, this oil can be useful for cleansing oily skins, strengthening nails or adding to baths.

Lanolin

- **Benefits** This is obtained from sheep's wool. Use the anhydrous version, without water, which, although it is very sticky to handle, nourishes and softens the skin.

- **Uses** Lanolin acts as an emulsifier as well as being ideal for rich moisturizers and conditioners for face, body and hands.

WARNING

Lanolin can cause an allergic reaction in some people. Carry out a patch-test before using, if you are unsure of how your skin will react, see pages 8-9.

OLIVE OIL

❊ **Benefits** This is a very fine, rich oil, particularly suitable for sensitive or very dry skin. It has a rather strong aroma.

❊ **Uses** Olive Oil can be used in face and body preparations and to condition hands, nails and lips.

SESAME OIL

❊ **Benefits** Sesame Oil, which has been used for thousands of years, is suitable for most skin types, including problem skin.

❊ **Uses** Do not use in quantities that add up to more than 10 per cent of all ingredients, see box on page 13, and do not buy the dark, roasted oil used in cooking as this can irritate the skin.

SUNFLOWER AND SAFFLOWER OILS

❊ **Benefits** These oils are both cheap and nourishing, so they can be used widely for a variety of preparations.

❊ **Uses** Use in baths, body oils, cleansers and moisturizers.

Sweet Almond Oil

❊ **Benefits** This fine, rich oil is suitable for most skin types. It has been used extensively throughout history on both face and body, to soothe, soften and nourish.

❊ **Uses** Sweet Almond Oil is ideal for removing make-up, helping eyelash growth, and for use in most preparations.

Wheatgerm Oil

❊ **Benefits** This rich and soothing oil can be effective for dry skin in particular. It is gentle enough to use around the eyes as a make-up remover or anti-wrinkle oil. The strong smell of this oil may be off-putting to some people. Wheatgerm oil can also cause allergies.

❊ **Uses** This oil has natural preservative qualities which makes it a useful addition to oil blends to prolong storage life. Do not use in quantities that add up to more than 10 per cent of all ingredients, see box on page 13.

Water Bases

Water plays an important role in looking after your skin. It is, of course, used for steaming and for beauty baths, but it also adds moisture to skin creams and lotions. When these preparations are used regularly, the moisture content helps to keep skin smooth and supple.

Natural water

This is most commonly used. Make sure it is bottled, purified or boiled to avoid contamination.

Rose Water and Orange Flower Water

These are both made from the distillation of flower petals and each has a beautiful fragrance. They are available from health food shops or herbal suppliers.

HERBAL WATERS

These are easy to make and can also be used on their own as mild skin cleansers or tonics. Choose herbs for their fragrance, or for their therapeutic properties.

SOME SUITABLE HERBS FOR HERBAL WATERS

Dry skin ELDER FLOWER • LIME FLOWER
Normal skin MARIGOLD • COMFREY
Oily skin CHAMOMILE • ROSEMARY

HERBAL WATER RECIPE

1. Place 50g (2oz/¼ cup) fresh herbs or flowers or 25g (1oz/⅛ cup) dried herbs or flowers in a china teapot kept specially for the purpose.
2. Pour over 300ml (½ pint/1¼ cups) boiling water. Cover and leave for 3 hours. Strain through filter paper or muslin before use.

STORING HERBAL WATERS

A Herbal Water should keep for up to 4 days if stored in the refrigerator, but use as soon as possible. Add 4 drops Simple Tincture of Benzoin per 120ml (4fl oz/½ cup) skin cream when including a Herbal Water, to ensure the keeping time.

Common Kitchen Ingredients

In addition to oil, wax and water bases, there are a number of other ingredients, found in most kitchens, that can be used to make natural skin care products. Use these on their own, mixed with each other, or blended with waxes, oils or water for an even more beneficial effect.

ALMONDS (GROUND)

- **Benefits** These can cleanse, soften, soothe and nourish the skin.
- **Uses** Use finely ground Almonds in scrubs, facial masks or in the bath.

BORAX

- **Benefits** This cleanses and is slightly astringent and antiseptic.
- **Uses** Borax is used for its emulsifying properties when combined with Beeswax to make skin care creams or lotions. It is always used sparingly in recipes.

CIDER VINEGAR

- **Benefits** This softens and soothes and can be useful for dry, itchy or flaky skin. It also helps to restore the protective acid mantle of the skin which acts as a barrier to infection.
- **Uses** Use diluted, 1 part Vinegar to 8 parts water, as a rinse or in skin tonics, cleansers or moisturizers.

GLYCERINE

- **Benefits** This softens, lubricates and moisturizes. It can be very helpful to dry skin and soothing to over-heated skin.
- **Uses** Glycerine is widely used in face, body and hand preparations.

HONEY

- **Benefits** This soothes, softens and nourishes, and can be helpful to dry hands and lips or over-heated skin.
- **Uses** Honey can be added to most recipes, used in the bath, or as a face mask on its own or with other ingredients.

MILK

- **Benefits** This cleanses, softens and nourishes and it is easily absorbed.
- **Uses** Use fresh or dried Milk for face masks, cleansers, moisturizers, or baths.

OATMEAL

- **Benefits** This soothes, softens and nourishes. Oatmeal is beneficial to most skin types, even sensitive skin.
- **Uses** Use finely ground Oatmeal for face masks, facial scrubs and in baths. It is an effective, but gentle, cleanser.

YOGHURT

- **Benefits** This cleanses, nourishes and is particularly suitable for normal to oily skin.
- **Uses** Use as a base for cleansers, face masks, facial scrubs or face and body moisturizers.

Other Useful Ingredients

The following ingredients are useful additions to those covered in the previous section. They can be obtained from most large chemists, drug stores, and herbal suppliers.

SIMPLE TINCTURE OF BENZOIN

- **Benefits** Alcohol is needed to release the properties of this tree resin and the resulting liquid is known as a 'Tincture'. Simple Tincture of Benzoin is antiseptic and soothing, helps to ease itching and can benefit blemished, cracked or dry skin.
- **Uses** Simple Tincture of Benzoin has natural preservative qualities, making it a useful addition to all types of preparation, particularly skin creams or lotions.

WARNING

Some people are allergic to Benzoin – particularly those who are allergic to plasters.

WITCH HAZEL

- **Benefits** This is astringent, antiseptic and soothing.
- **Uses** Witch Hazel can be used on its own, or with other ingredients, to make skin tonics or creams for normal or oily skin.

— 2 —

Adding Fragrance

Aromatic extracts of plants have been used since the time of the Ancient Egyptians. Essential Oils, the pure, highly concentrated essences of plants now used for their therapeutic qualities, also provide a wide range of fragrances for use in natural skin care products. You could use just one Essential Oil to perfume an entire range of products, choose a different fragrance for each preparation or leave them fragrance-free. Experiment to see which scents and therapeutic options appeal to you.

USING ESSENTIAL OILS SAFELY

You should always use these oils with care, following the guidelines given opposite. These are for general information only and for further guidance you should consult a qualified Aromatherapist.

- Always use 100 per cent pure Essential Oils and measure out oils in drops. Never use Essential Oils directly on the skin undiluted, as they are very potent.
- Avoid contact with eyes and do not take internally.
- Keep out of reach of children.
- Store in a cool, dark place with lids tightly fitted, and do not store in plastic containers or on varnished surfaces.
- Seek medical advice before using Essential Oils if you have particularly sensitive or allergic skin.
- Consult an expert before using Essential Oils during pregnancy or if you are receiving treatment for any medical condition, as some oils can be harmful if not used correctly or appropriately.
- Do not use Citrus Essential Oils before exposure to the sun or before using a sunbed. You should wait at least six hours before doing so and shower first. These oils can irritate some sensitive skins: always use only half the drops recommended for other oils. Do not use in the bath.

CITRUS OILS

Bergamot • Grapefruit • Lemon • Mandarin • Orange

CHOOSING ESSENTIAL OILS TO SUIT YOUR SKIN

Suitable for most skins GERANIUM • LAVENDER • PALMAROSA • ROSEMARY
Oily to Normal skin CYPRESS • LEMON • ORANGE • YLANG-YLANG
Dry to Normal skin NEROLI • PATCHOULI • SANDALWOOD • ROSE

HOW TO INCLUDE ESSENTIAL OILS

- **For a skin care cream** Add an Essential Oil once the cream has thickened. Ensure that it is thoroughly mixed in.
- **For a skin care oil** Add an Essential Oil with the base oils and shake the bottle thoroughly to blend them together.

Quantities to use

For face oil A maximum total of 5 drops per 30ml (1fl oz/2 tbsp).
For body oil A maximum total of 15 drops per 60ml (2fl oz/4 tbsp).
For skin care cream A maximum total of 6 drops per 120ml (4fl oz/½ cup).
For bath oil A maximum total of 30 drops per 30ml (1fl oz/2 tbsp). Use 1 tsp blended oil in the bath. Alternatively, add a maximum of 4 drops of Essential Oil directly to the bath, adding the Essential Oil once the bath is full and agitatating well to disperse before getting in.

A RANGE OF ESSENTIAL OILS

To help you decide which Essential Oils to use in natural skin care products, the list opposite describes the qualities of a range of oils, the type of skin they can benefit and the kind of fragrance they have.

CHAMOMILE, GERMAN
MATRICARIA RECUTITA

- **Therapeutic properties** Calming, relaxing, soothing. Helpful to dry, sensitive, mature, problem and inflamed skin.
- **Aroma** Herbaceous, sweet, warm

GERANIUM
PELARGONIUM GRAVEOLENS

- **Therapeutic properties** Uplifting, toning, calming, refreshing, relaxing. Helpful to most skin types including problem skins.
- **Aroma** Floral, sweet

WARNING

Some people are allergic to this oil.

GRAPEFRUIT
CITRUS PARADISI

- **Therapeutic properties** Revitalizing, refreshing, uplifting. Helpful to weak nails and for toning the skin.
- **Aroma** Tangy, fresh, sweet

WARNING

This is a Citrus Oil – follow the instructions for use on page 25.

LAVENDER

LAVANDULA ANGUSTIFOLIA

- **Therapeutic properties** Uplifting, soothing, relaxing, stimulating. Helpful to most skin types, including problem and sensitive skin.
- **Aroma** Herbaceous, sweet

LEMON

CITRUS LIMON

- **Therapeutic properties** Astringent, refreshing, revitalizing. Helpful to oily, blemished or mature skin and wrinkles.
- **Aroma** Fresh, sharp, clean, tangy

NEROLI

CITRUS AURANTIUM BIGARADIA

- **Therapeutic properties** Unwinding, uplifting, relaxing. Helpful to most skin types and to stretch marks and broken capillaries.
- **Aroma** Floral, fresh, sweet, warm

ORANGE

CITRUS SINENSIS

- **Therapeutic properties** Refreshing, uplifting, toning, relaxing. Helpful to oily, mature or dull skin and also to wrinkles.
- **Aroma** Sweet, fresh, warm

WARNING – LEMON AND ORANGE OILS

These are Citrus Oils – follow the instructions for use on page 25.

PALMAROSA

CYMBOPOGON MARTINI

- **Therapeutic properties** Uplifting and reviving. Helpful to minor skin irritations and problem skin.
- **Aroma** Floral, tangy, sweet

SANDALWOOD

SANTALUM ALBUM

- **Therapeutic properties** Calming, uplifting, relaxing. Helpful to dry, chapped, cracked, or problem skin.
- **Aroma** Woody, sweet, warm

YLANG-YLANG

CANANGA ODORATA

- **Therapeutic properties** Uplifting, relaxing, soothing, calming. Helpful to most skin types.
- **Aroma** Sweet, warm, floral, exotic

WARNING

Ylang-ylang can cause headaches and nausea in some people, particularly those who find some perfumes trigger headaches.

— 3 —

Skin Creams

Making your own cleansing, moisturizing and conditioning face and body creams from a blend of waxes, oils and water is a very satisfying pastime. These products are simple to make, but look so professional that everyone will be amazed to learn that you have created them yourself.

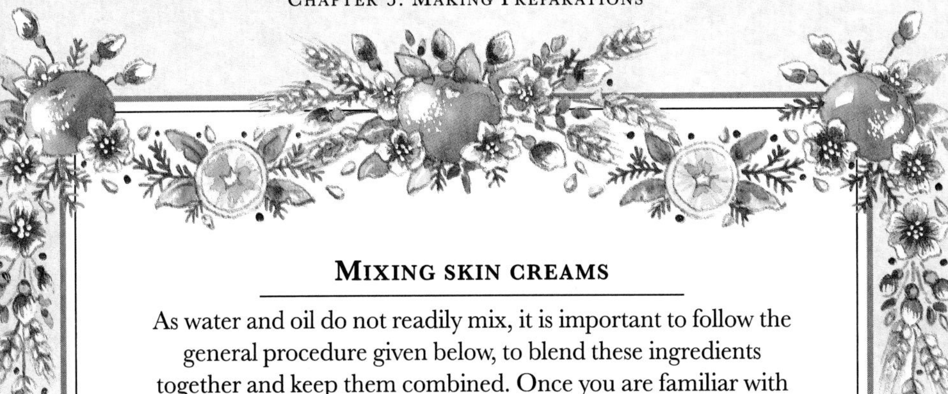

MIXING SKIN CREAMS

As water and oil do not readily mix, it is important to follow the general procedure given below, to blend these ingredients together and keep them combined. Once you are familiar with this process, you will find creating skin creams is very straightforward.

What you need

- A large bain-marie or water bath
  A roasting pan can be used instead, but whatever container you use, it must be suitable for heating on the stove and large enough to hold two bowls.
- Two heat-proof bowls
  Using two bowls ensures that oil and wax in one bowl and water in the other are heated to the same temperature.
- Set of measuring spoons
  This makes measuring quick and easy.
- Wooden spoon, hand whisk or electric mixer.
- Tinted glass jars with screw tops and labels

HOW TO MIX SKIN CREAMS

1 **Heating the ingredients** Two-thirds fill the water bath with water and add the bowls – one containing the waxes and/or oils and the other containing the water and Borax. Bring the water in the bath to simmering (not boiling) point and heat the bowl contents until the waxes have melted and the oils and water are warm. Depending on the ingredients used, this takes about 5 minutes.

2 **Mixing the cream** Wearing oven gloves, remove the bowls from the heat and slowly add the water to the waxes and/or oil, stirring all the time. As they combine the mixture will turn white. You can use a wooden spoon for mixing but it is quicker to use a hand whisk and easier still to use an electric mixer. Continue to mix the ingredients until the cream thickens and cools. While mixing, you can place the bowl in cold water to speed up the cooling process.

3 **Adding a natural preservative** At this stage you can add a few drops of Simple Tincture of Benzoin, to act as a preservative. Use in the proportion of 4 drops Benzoin to 120ml (4fl oz/½ cup) cream mixture. Stir in well.

4 **Including a fragrance** Now is the time to add a fragrant Essential Oil, if you wish. Use in a proportion of a maximum total of 6 drops Essential Oil to 120ml (4fl oz/½ cup) cream. Mix in thoroughly.

5 **Bottling and storing** Once the cream is cool, spoon into tinted glass jars with screw tops and label. Your skin cream is now ready to use. The mixture should last approximately two months, depending on the ingredients used. It is best kept in the refrigerator to ensure freshness.

WHAT WENT WRONG?

The ingredients don't combine

This can occur if the cream cools too quickly. Try mixing the cream for a longer period. Alternatively, reheat the mixture in the water bath and try blending again. This may also occur if the water is added too quickly with insufficient beating or stirring.

The consistency is too thin or too thick

This is generally due to a slight inaccuracy in measuring out the ingredients. But the right consistency is not essential. You can still use the cream, even if it has a different texture – you may even prefer it that way.

The cream feels gritty when used

This can occur when the Borax in the recipe has not been completely mixed into the water. Make sure you stir the Borax in very thoroughly until it is dissolved.

Experimenting with Variations

The joy of making your own skin care products is that you can tailor-make them to suit the needs of your own particular skin, even varying them to suit the skin on different parts of your face and body. It may take some trial and error at first to get the products just as you want them. But by using the information and recipes in this book as guidelines, you will soon be able to make a wide range of products individually created to meet your needs.

WAXES AND OILS

Choose from the wide variety of Vegetable and Nut Oils suggested, see pages 12-17. Use the information to help you choose which wax or oil will best suit your skin, any particular skin problem and the type of preparation you are making.

WATER

Instead of always using natural water, you can substitute Rose Water, Orange Flower Water or a Herbal Water in any recipe in which water is listed as an ingredient, see pages 18-19.

ESSENTIAL OILS

The simplest way to individualize a recipe is by choosing your own fragrance. You can pick an Essential Oil for its aroma, for its therapeutic properties, to match the Herb or Flower Water that you have used or to tie in with a range of products that you are making. See pages 24-29 for more on Essential Oils.

CHANGING THE TEXTURE

Although the recipes have many of the same ingredients, by changing one ingredient or by changing the proportions you can change the texture of your product and, for example, turn a cleansing cream into a cleansing lotion.

VARYING THE QUANTITY

You can make up as little or as much of each product as you want. If you use up one cream quickly, you can double the quantity next time you make it. Conversely, if it takes a long time to finish a preparation halve the amount. But ensure that you make only enough of a skin care product so that you always use it fresh.

KEEPING A RECORD

Keep a notebook to write down recipes. Not only will this enable you to recreate preparations at a later date, but you can use it as a reference source for further experiments.

Storing Preparations

Making your own skin care preparations means that you have complete control over what you put on your skin. Because you have made them yourself you will know that the ingredients are natural and fresh and that they suit your skin. However, bear in mind that, by avoiding commercial preservatives and additives, the products will not last as long as those you buy in the shops. Clean equipment and good storage are vital.

Making your own natural skin care products allows you to use them regularly and generously. So you will probably find you have used them up long before they have had the chance to become rancid.

HOW TO STORE CREAMS AND LOTIONS

- Use opaque glass jars with tightly fitting lids to prevent light and air reaching the contents and causing deterioration. Re-useable brown glass jars and bottles are available to buy, or you can save and wash empty glass jars from cosmetics that you bought previously.
- Ensure that storage containers and utensils are all thoroughly clean. Wash jars in (fairly) hot, soapy water. Thoroughly rinse, then dry them out in a very low-temperature oven.

- Keeping your preparations in the refrigerator will help them to last longer, particularly if your home is warm. If you find this inconvenient you can always have a small pot available for immediate use while refrigerating the rest.
- Use a spoon or spatula instead of dipping your fingers into creams. This prevents dirt or bacteria on your fingers from getting into preparations you have made.
- Always label a jar or bottle immediately after filling it, especially if you are making more than one product at a time. It is very easy to forget which is which when confronted with a mass of anonymous pots of cream. Use plain sticky labels or your own home-made labels, decorating them with attractive photo-copied and coloured designs to make the finished effect look very professional. It is a good idea to include the date you made the product on the label. Add a Not to be Eaten or Drunk warning to the label for safety.

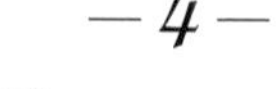

Cleansing

Cleansing is, probably, the most essential part of any skin care routine and should be done at the beginning and, even more importantly, at the end of each day. In the morning, cleansing freshens the skin. In the evening, it removes the day's dirt, grime and make-up that can block the pores and lead to blemishes, spots or inflammation.

HOW TO APPLY CLEANSER

- **Cream cleansers** Apply these with clean fingertips, in small upward and outward circular movements. After about half a minute remove from the skin with a tissue or damp cotton wool.
- **Cleansing liquids, lotions or oils** Apply with cotton wool. Leave on the skin for about half a minute before removing with a tissue or damp cotton wool.

SOME SIMPLE CLEANSERS TO TRY

- **For oily to normal skins** Apply 7.5m (½tbsp) Yoghurt with your fingertips. Rinse off with water after half a minute.
- **For dry to normal skins** Apply Milk with cotton wool and leave for half a minute before rinsing off with tepid water.

CLEANSING CREAM RECIPE

This makes about 240ml (8fl oz/1 cup) of fluffy, soft cream that is suitable for most skin types.

1. Heat 150ml (5fl oz/⅔ cup) water in a bowl in a water bath. Add 2.5ml (½ tsp) Borax and mix it in thoroughly. At the same time, heat 25g (1 oz) grated Beeswax and 180ml (6fl oz/¾ cup) Sweet Almond Oil in a separate bowl in the same water bath, until the wax melts.
2. Remove both bowls from the heat and pour the water into the oils, stirring constantly. Continue to mix the cream until it thickens and cools.
3. Add 8-12 drops of Essential Oil and 8 drops of Simple Tincture of Benzoin making sure that they blend in completely. Beat the cream until cool, then spoon into a pot.

- A smoother cream will be obtained by using Emulsifying Wax in place of Beeswax.

Oils as Cleansers

As an alternative to a cleansing cream or lotion, use a Vegetable or Nut Oil. This is a very simple way to cleanse your skin and remove make-up. Experiment to see which option most suits your skin. Oils can be used individually or in combination and if you make up a bottle of cleansing oil, an Essential Oil can also be added.

CLEANSING OILS FOR DIFFERENT SKIN TYPES

Oily to normal skin SUNFLOWER • SWEET ALMOND
Dry to normal skin AVOCADO • WHEATGERM

CLEANSING ESSENTIAL OILS

CLARY SAGE • GERANIUM • LAVENDER • LEMON

GRAPESEED CLEANSING OIL RECIPE

This makes about 60ml (2fl oz/4 tbsp) of a general purpose cleanser that can also remove make-up.

1 Pour 5 ml (1 tsp) Wheatgerm Oil, 10ml (⅓fl oz/2 tsp) each of Sesame Oil and Sweet Almond Oil and 30ml (1fl oz/2 tbsp) Grapeseed Oil into a bottle.

2 Add a maximum total of 3 drops of Essential Oil, shake thoroughly to mix, and apply with cotton wool.

- Wheatgerm Oil can be blended into any face or body oil recipe to act as a preservative, helping to prolong the keeping time of the preparation. Use it in a proportion of no more than 10 per cent of the total ingredients, see page 13.

SWEET ALMOND EYE MAKE-UP REMOVER RECIPE

This makes 120ml (4fl oz/½ cup) of a very gentle, oily make-up remover for the delicate skin around the eyes. Apply the oil with cotton wool, gently wiping in a circle from the inner corner of the eyelid, around the outer edge of the eye and back under the eye to the nose. Never drag the skin around the eye as this can lead to wrinkling. This oil is deliberately left unperfumed for its use in such a sensitive area.

1 Pour 30ml (1fl oz/2 tbsp) Castor Oil and 90ml (3fl oz/6 tbsp) Sweet Almond Oil into a bottle.

2 Blend together by shaking the bottle.

- Castor Oil is also a good conditioner for weak eyelashes.

WARNING

Do not add Essential Oil to this Eye Make-up Remover Recipe.

Face masks cleanse, stimulate and nourish skin, helping to clear blemishes and leave the skin smooth and soft. You can use a facial mask once a week to help to restore and freshen your skin. Experiment to find the ideal mask for your skin. Many of the foods found in the kitchen can be turned to good use as quick, easy-to-make, and very cheap face masks.

INGREDIENTS FOR FACE MASKS

APPLE • APRICOT • AVOCADO • BANANA • CORNMEAL • CUCUMBER
GRAPE • GROUND ALMONDS • GROUND RICE • HONEY • MANGO
MELON • OATMEAL • PEACH • PLUM • STRAWBERRY • TOMATO
Most kinds of fruit can be added. Mash before including in a mask.

ADDITIONAL LIQUID INGREDIENTS

For dry to normal skin EGG YOLK • MILK • VEGETABLE AND NUT OILS

For oily to normal skin CIDER VINEGAR • CITRUS FRUIT JUICE (GRAPEFRUIT, LEMON, ORANGE) • EGG WHITE • YOGHURT

How to make a face mask

Mix your chosen ingredients to produce a mask that is thick enough to stay in place on your face, but not so thick as to drag the skin when applying. A little goes a long way and generally less than 5ml (1 tsp) of each ingredient is needed, although this depends on the number and type of ingredients used. Make up only enough mixture for use in one treatment as it will not keep.

How to apply a face mask

1 Tie back your hair and cleanse your skin to remove dirt and make-up.

2 Apply the mixed ingredients to your face by gently patting them on with your fingertips. Do not drag the skin as you apply the mask and ensure that you avoid the delicate eye and mouth areas.

3 Leave the mask in place to dry for 15-20 minutes. Remove with tepid water, either splashed on with the hands or applied with cotton wool. Once your face is clean, close the pores with a skin tonic.

Facial Scrubs

Facial scrubs are gently abrasive, helping to stimulate the skin, improve the circulation and remove dead skin cells which can clog up pores. Using a scrub regularly can help to leave your skin feeling clean and smooth. You can easily make a scrub from foods found in the kitchen. Use just one ingredient or combine a few.

INGREDIENTS FOR FACIAL SCRUBS

BRAN • CORNMEAL • GROUND ALMONDS • GROUND DRIED CITRUS PEEL (GRAPEFRUIT, LEMON, ORANGE) • GROUND SUNFLOWER SEEDS OATFLAKES • OATMEAL • SALT • WHEATGERM.

HOW TO MAKE A FACIAL SCRUB

- Combine your chosen dry ingredients to make up the scrub base. You can make more than you need and store it in a pot ready for use whenever you want it.
- To use the scrub, mix up about 2.5ml (½ tsp) of the base with a little water, Yoghurt, Milk, Cream or Vegetable or Nut Oil to make a paste. Mix up only enough for each use as it will not keep once the liquid ingredients are added.

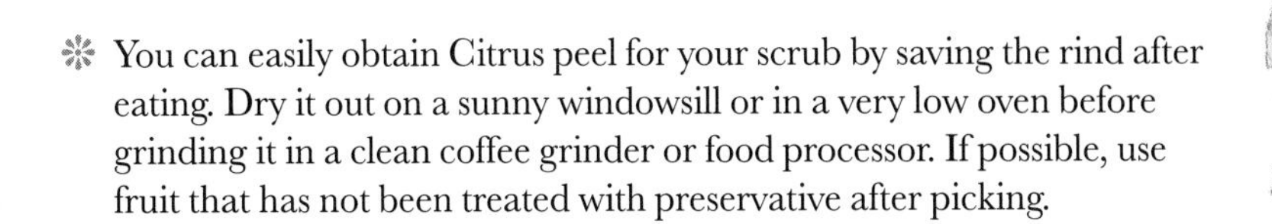

❊ You can easily obtain Citrus peel for your scrub by saving the rind after eating. Dry it out on a sunny windowsill or in a very low oven before grinding it in a clean coffee grinder or food processor. If possible, use fruit that has not been treated with preservative after picking.

HOW TO APPLY A FACIAL SCRUB

Apply the scrub with small upward and outward circular movements, gently using your fingertips. Avoid the delicate eye and mouth areas. Leave the scrub for a minute or so before rinsing off, with tepid water.

ORANGE AND LEMON FACIAL SCRUB RECIPE

1 Mix together 45ml (1½fl oz/3 tbsp) each of finely ground Oatmeal, finely ground Almonds and finely ground dried Orange and/or Lemon peel and store this deliciously fragrant scrub in a 120ml (4fl oz/½ cup) pot.

2 Mix 2.5ml (½ tsp) of facial scrub with enough water or Milk to make a paste in the palm of your hand. Apply with the fingertips in small circular movements. Alternatively, sprinkle a small amount of facial scrub onto damp fingertips and apply in the same way. Rinse off after one minute.

- This scrub can also be used as a base for a face mask.

Skin tonics are used after cleansing to remove the last traces of cleanser and any remaining dirt, to freshen the skin and close the pores. Use a skin tonic in the morning or at any time during the day.

INGREDIENTS FOR SKIN TONICS

Herbal Waters

These are gentle enough to be used as skin fresheners, see page 18-19.

- **For normal to oily skin** To 300ml (½pint/1¼ cups) Herbal Water add 30ml (1fl oz/2 tbsp) Witch Hazel.
- **For very oily skin** To 300ml (½pint/1¼ cups) Herbal Water add 15ml (½fl oz/1 tbsp) Vodka.

Cider Vinegar

When diluted, this makes a very useful skin tonic that helps to restore the skin's protective acid mantle.

- Add 15ml (½fl oz/1 tbsp) Cider Vinegar to 120ml (4fl oz/½cup) water, Rose Water, Orange Flower Water or Herbal Water for a refreshing skin tonic for all skin types.

Rose Water and Witch Hazel

These form the base for many skin tonics, but they can also be used on their own. Rose Water is a very gentle tonic suitable for dry to normal skin, while Witch Hazel is more astringent and can benefit oily to normal skin.

HOW TO APPLY SKIN TONICS

Apply skin tonic with cotton wool in smooth upward strokes, or, alternatively, splash on with your hands.

ROSE WATER AND WITCH HAZEL TONER RECIPE

This makes 120ml (4fl oz/½ cup) of a fragrant, refreshing toner. Orange Flower Water or a Herbal Water can be used instead of Rose Water.

1. Pour 90ml (3fl oz/6 tbsp) Rose Water and 30ml (1fl oz/2 tbsp) Witch Hazel into a bottle.
2. Shake to combine.

- **For dry to normal skin** Add several drops of Glycerine.
- **For oily to normal skin** Add 5ml (1tsp) Cider Vinegar or use equal amounts of Rose Water and Witch Hazel.

Using a moisturizer every day helps to keep skin smooth and soft. All skin types can benefit from moisturizing, even oily skins. A moisturizer helps to replace moisture lost from the skin as well as protecting it from environmental damage caused by central heating, pollution and hot and cold weather.

Simple moisturizers

Apply a thin film of Vegetable or Nut Oil over the skin. Splash with water before blotting dry.

How to apply moisturizer

Once you have cleansed and toned your skin, apply moisturizer in gentle upward and outward circular strokes, massaging it into the skin. Don't forget to moisturize your neck, using smooth upward strokes, as well as your entire body.

ALMOND AND AVOCADO MOISTURIZER RECIPE

This makes 180ml (6fl oz/¾ cup) of a very smooth, easily absorbed, light cream, suitable for most skin types.

1 Melt 20ml (⅔fl oz/4 tsp) Emulsifying Wax, 10ml (⅓fl oz/2 tsp) grated Beeswax, 40ml (1⅓fl oz/8 tsp) Avocado Oil and 80ml (2⅔fl oz/⅓ cup) Sweet Almond Oil in a bowl in a water bath. At the same time, heat 60ml (2fl oz/4 tbsp) water in a second bowl. Add a pinch of Borax to the water and mix thoroughly.

2 Remove the bowls from the heat. Slowly pour the water into the wax and oil, beating all the time. Beat until the cream thickens and cools before adding a maximum total of 4 drops of Essential Oil of your choice. Stir in well.

ORANGE FLOWER MOISTURIZER RECIPE

This makes about 60ml (2fl oz/4 tbsp) of light, non-greasy, soft cream that is very easy to make and is suitable for most skins, particularly normal and oily types.

1 Heat 15ml (½fl oz/1 tbsp) each of Sweet Almond Oil and Emulsifying Wax with 2.5ml (½tsp) Lanolin in a bowl in a water bath. At the same time, heat 2.5ml (½tsp) Witch Hazel, 3.75ml (¾ tsp) Glycerine and 60ml (2fl oz/4 tbsp) Orange Flower Water in a separate bowl. Add 1.25ml (¼ tsp) Borax to the Witch Hazel mixture, ensuring that it mixes in completely.

2 Remove the bowls from the heat; mix the Witch Hazel mixture into the oils. This cream thickens quickly. Once cool, add a maximum total of 3 drops of Essential Oil of your choice, stir well, and transfer to a 60ml (2fl oz/4 tbsp) jar.

Conditioning and Nourishing

Conditioning and nourishing creams are richer and thicker than moisturizers and, with regular use, can make the skin feel soft and supple. These more intensive creams are used less often than regular moisturizer – once a week is usually adequate for normal skins.

HOW TO APPLY CONDITIONING CREAM

Smooth the cream onto your face, using gentle upward and outward circular movements, and onto your neck with smooth, upward strokes. Leave for about 15 minutes before dabbing off any residue with a tissue. The cream can occasionally be left on overnight for a deeper treatment, but ensure that you protect your pillow.

COCONUT OIL CONDITIONING CREAM RECIPE

This makes 120ml (4fl oz/½ cup) of soft cream with a very fine consistency.

1 Heat 15ml (½fl oz/1 tbsp) grated Beeswax, 90ml (3fl oz/6 tbsp) Coconut Oil, 60ml (2fl oz/4 tbsp) Olive Oil and 30ml (1fl oz/2 tbsp) Sweet Almond Oil in a bowl standing in a water bath. At the same time, heat 120ml (4fl oz/½ cup) water in a separate bowl. Thoroughly mix 5ml (1 tsp) Borax into the water while heating.

2 Remove from the heat and slowly mix the water with the oils, beating all the time. Continue to beat lightly until the cream is cool and completely smooth. Mix in a maximum total of 4 drops of the Essential Oil of your choice and spoon into a pot.

CARROT OIL NOURISHING CREAM RECIPE

This makes 120ml (4fl oz/½ cup) of a soft, rich and nourishing orange-coloured cream.

1 Melt 7.5ml (¼fl oz/½ tbsp) each of Lanolin, Emulsifying Wax and grated Beeswax, with 22.5ml (¾fl oz/1½tbsp) each of Carrot Oil and Wheatgerm Oil in a bowl standing in a water bath. At the same time, in a separate bowl, heat 45ml (1½fl oz/3 tbsp) water, thoroughly mixing in 1.25ml (¼tsp) Borax.

2 Remove from the heat and mix the water into the oils. Beat the cream until it thickens and cools before adding 4 drops of Simple Tincture of Benzoin and a maximum total of 6 drops of Essential Oil such as Mandarin or Orange. Spoon into a pot for storage.

— 5 —

Body Conditioning

Like your face, your whole body can benefit from regular nourishing to restore the condition of the skin. Use creams, lotions or oils liberally all over the body. Apply with the fingertips in smooth upward strokes over the arms and legs, upwards and outwards over the trunk and across the shoulders. Body conditioners are most effective when applied after a bath.

SIMPLE BODY CONDITIONERS

- Use a loofah or a well-wrung out, damp face cloth to help remove dead skin cells and improve circulation.
- Gently rub in dairy Cream, Milk, Rose Water or Glycerine to help nourish the skin.

ROSE WATER MOISTURIZER RECIPE

This recipe makes about 180ml (6fl oz/¾ cup)of a fragrant, refreshing, non-oily body moisturizer.

1. Beat together 60ml (2fl oz/4 tbsp) Glycerine and 180ml (6fl oz/¾ cup) Rose Water.
2. Pour into a bottle and label. Experiment with the quantities of these two ingredients until you find the right balance for your skin.

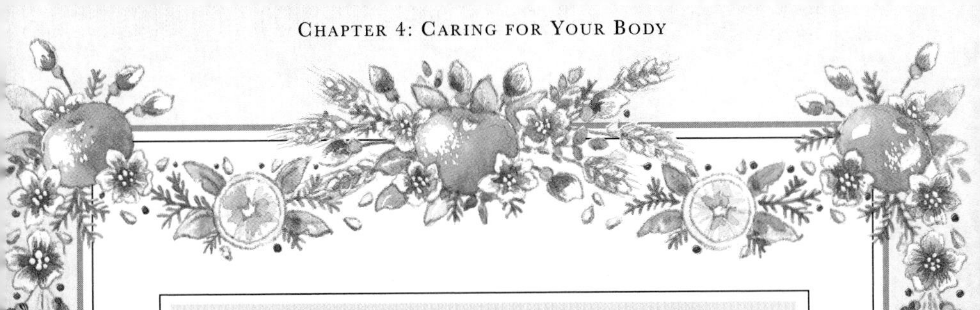

ALMOND OIL BODY LOTION RECIPE

This recipe makes about 60ml (2fl oz/4 tbsp) of a light, easily absorbed body lotion.

1 Warm 75ml (2½fl oz/5 tbsp) Rose Water in a bowl placed in a water bath and thoroughly mix in 2.5ml (½ tsp) Borax. In a separate bowl, at the same time, warm 30ml (1fl oz/2 tbsp) Sweet Almond Oil.

2 Remove from the heat, add the Rose Water slowly to the oil and beat until cool. These ingredients can easily separate so ensure that you continue to mix them until they are thoroughly blended. Add a maximum total of 3 drops of Essential Oil and stir well. Shake well before use.

MASSAGE OILS

One of the simplest ways to nourish the skin on your body is to massage in Vegetable or Nut Oil, either singly or in combination. Pour a small amount into the palm of your hand or make up a bottle of massage oil, adding Essential Oils if you prefer. Use a maximum total of 15 drops Essential Oil in 60ml (2fl oz/4 tbsp) body oil.

OILS TO USE FOR BODY MASSAGE

APRICOT • GRAPESEED • SUNFLOWER • SWEET ALMOND

In addition to looking after the body generally, there are a few areas that need extra help – the hard-working hands, nails, elbows, knees and feet. However, spending time giving these special attention soon restores the condition of the skin.

HANDS

- Rub Lemon Juice or a slice of Lemon over your hands to cleanse, smooth and deodorize.
- Soak hands in a bowl of Milk or diluted Cider Vinegar (1 part Vinegar to 8 parts water) for 5 minutes to soothe and soften skin which is rough or chapped.

COCONUT OIL HAND CREAM RECIPE

This makes 120ml (4fl oz/½ cup) of a silky, easily absorbed, firm cream

1. Melt 90ml (3fl oz/6 tbsp) grated Beeswax and 120ml (4fl oz/½ cup) each of Sweet Almond Oil and Coconut Oil in a bowl standing in a water bath. Slowly add 180ml (6fl oz/¾ cup) Glycerine. When warm, remove from the heat and beat until thickened and cool.
2. Add a maximum total of 6 drops of Essential Oil – Grapefruit has a wonderfully fresh fragrance. Pot in a 120ml (4fl oz/½ cup) jar.

NAILS

- Soak fingertips in warm Olive Oil or Cider Vinegar for 5 minutes.

GLYCERINE NAIL CONDITIONER RECIPE

This makes 60ml (2fl oz/4 tbsp) of a wonderful conditioner. Apply using cotton wool all over the nail and cuticle to help strengthen the nails and soften the cuticles.

1. Pour 30ml (1fl oz/2 tbsp) each of Castor Oil and Glycerine into a bottle. You could also add 12 drops of infused Carrot Oil and/or a maximum total of 8 drops of Lemon Essential Oil if you wish.
2. Shake the bottle thoroughly to mix.

ELBOWS, KNEES AND FEET

- Rub a slice of Lemon over these areas to clean, smooth and soften rough skin.
- Lemon Juice or Cider Vinegar can be added to a foot bath to soften the skin and help relieve tiredness.

HONEY LIP BALM RECIPE

This makes about 90 ml (3fl oz/6 tbsp) of an excellent firm balm for chapped or dry lips.

1. Melt 90ml (3fl oz/6 tbsp) grated Beeswax, 90ml (3fl oz/6 tbsp) Sesame Oil and 30ml (1fl oz/2 tbsp) Honey in a bowl in a water-bath.
2. Remove from the heat and stir until thickened.

Bathing

Taking a bath is not just a means of getting clean, it can also be a way of relaxing, energizing, soothing, softening or nourishing your body. There are so many simple-to-add ingredients you can include in a bath, to transform every bath into a valuable treatment for your body.

Some simple bath additions

To soothe and soften the skin add to your bath 15ml (½fl oz/1 tbsp) powdered Milk, ground Almonds or Oatmeal, **or** 150ml (5fl oz/⅔ cup) Cider Vinegar.

Bath oils

Adding 5ml (1 tsp) of a Vegetable or Nut Oil to a bath can nourish the skin. These oils float on the surface of the water, adhering to the body as you emerge. Use the oils singly or in combination, pouring them straight into the bath.

Alternatively, make up a bottle of bath oil, adding Essential Oils if you wish. Use a maximum of 10 drops of Essential Oil per 10ml (2 tsp) of bath oil. Use 5ml (1 tsp) of the blend in a bath.

OILS TO USE IN THE BATH

GRAPESEED • SESAME • SUNFLOWER • SWEET ALMOND
TURKEY RED

ESSENTIAL OILS TO ADD TO A BATH OIL

Relaxing SANDALWOOD • YLANG-YLANG
Calming CHAMOMILE • LAVENDER
Uplifting GERANIUM • NEROLI

APRICOT BATH OIL RECIPE

This makes just under 30ml (1fl oz/2 tbsp) of bath oil.
Use 5ml (1tsp) of the blend in a bath.

1 Pour 15ml (½fl oz/1 tbsp) Sweet Almond Oil and 5ml (1 tsp) each of Apricot Oil and Avocado Oil into a bottle.

2 Add a maximum total of 25 drops of Essential Oil and shake well to mix.

WARNING

Using oils in this way can make the bath slippery – take extra care when getting in or out.

— 6 —

A–Z of Skin Care

The ingredients used in natural skin care preparations can ease minor skin conditions, gently soothing and restoring the skin. Use this guide to help you choose the ingredients to make preparations that are beneficial to both your skin type and any present skin condition.

Before incorporating any of the ingredients recommended on the following pages in recipes turn to the relevant chapter covering how to include them. For more information on Simple aids see Common Kitchen Ingredients, pages 20-22 and Other Useful Ingredients, page 23; for Essential Oils, see pages 24-29; for Vegetable and Nut Oils, see pages 12-17; for Herbal Waters, see page 19.

These suggestions are given for information purposes only. For any serious or persistent skin complaint you should seek medical advice.

AFTER-SUN SOOTHERS

Always take precautions to protect the skin against the harmful effects of too much sun. If, after sitting in the sun, you feel unwell or have sunburn, seek medical advice immediately. If you overheat from spending time in the sun, cool your skin with one of these ingredients.

What to use

Simple aids CIDER VINEGAR • CUCUMBER • GLYCERINE HONEY • MILK • ROSE WATER • TEA • YOGHURT

Essential Oils CHAMOMILE • GERANIUM • LAVENDER • ROSE

Herbs CHAMOMILE • COMFREY • ELDER FLOWER • MARIGOLD

BLEMISHED SKIN

Spots or blemishes often appear on the chin and forehead. The texture of blemished skin also tends to be coarse with open pores.

What to use

Simple aids SIMPLE TINCTURE OF BENZOIN OATMEAL • PEAR • RASPBERRY • YOGHURT

Essential Oils BERGAMOT • CHAMOMILE • GERANIUM LAVENDER • PALMAROSA • SANDALWOOD

Vegetable/Nut Oils CARROT • COCONUT GRAPESEED • SWEET ALMOND

Herbs COMFREY • MARIGOLD • PARSLEY • SAGE • YARROW

COMBINATION SKIN

When both dry and greasy areas are present on the face, this is known as combination skin. Typically the areas of oiliness are in a T-shaped panel across the forehead and down the nose and chin, with patches of dry, sensitive skin on the cheeks. It is wise to treat each of these areas individually as either 'dry' or 'oily'.

What to use

See either Dry or Oily Skin, whichever is appropriate.

DRY SKIN

Dry skin shows up in dry, flaky, rough skin that feels tight and stretched after it has been washed with soap and water. It may also be sensitive, itchy and lacking elasticity, and can lead to premature wrinkles. A dry skin can greatly benefit from regular nourishing.

What to use

Simple aids CIDER VINEGAR • GLYCERINE • OATMEAL • ROSE WATER
Essential Oils CHAMOMILE • GERANIUM • ROSE • SANDALWOOD
Vegetable/Nut Oils AVOCADO • APRICOT • CARROT
OLIVE • WHEATGERM
Herbs ELDER FLOWERS • LIME FLOWERS

Hands

Regular moisturizing and conditioning of hands can have wonderful results, helping to combat the daily wear and tear that can lead to dry, chapped, roughened or cracked hands.

What to use

Simple aids Ground Almonds • Cider Vinegar • Glycerine Honey • Lemon • Oatmeal • Rose Water

Essential Oils Geranium • Lemon • Lavender • Sandalwood

Vegetable/Nut Oils Carrot • Grapeseed • Lanolin • Olive Sweet Almond • Wheatgerm

Lips

Lips easily become dry and chapped from ill-health, central heating, cold weather or too much sun. Soothing and softening them with balms and oils helps to relieve soreness and restore their condition.

What to Use

Simple aids Honey • Rose Water

Essential Oils Chamomile • Geranium • Lavender

Vegetable/Nut Oils Castor • Carrot • Coconut • Olive Sesame • Sweet Almond

MATURE SKIN

Mature skin tends to have a loss of elasticity and firmness leading to lines and wrinkles, particularly around the eyes and mouth. The skin may also be very dry, so regular moisturizing and nourishing can be beneficial.

What to Use

Simple aids WATER MELON JUICE

Essential Oils GERANIUM • LAVENDER • ROSE • SANDALWOOD

Vegetable/Nut and other Oils AVOCADO • CARROT
LANOLIN • SESAME • WHEATGERM

NAILS

The growing area of nails is just below the base of the nail, so massaging this area with nourishing oils or creams can help to stimulate growth and strengthen nails. Wear protective gloves when using household detergents and cleansers to help prevent any damage to nails.

What to use

Simple aids CIDER VINEGAR • LEMON JUICE

Essential Oils LAVENDER • LEMON • GRAPEFRUIT • ROSEMARY

Vegetable/Nut and other Oils APRICOT • AVOCADO • CARROT •
GRAPESEED, LANOLIN • OLIVE • SWEET ALMOND

OILY SKIN

Oily skin is often characterized by a shiny surface which may be sallow looking and it also has a tendency to spots and open pores. Regular cleansing is important for this type of skin.

What to use

Simple aids CIDER VINEGAR • CUCUMBER • LEMON JUICE • OATMEAL WITCH HAZEL • YOGHURT

Essential Oils GERANIUM • LEMON • YLANG-YLANG

Vegetable/Nut and other Oils COCONUT • GRAPESEED SWEET ALMOND

SENSITIVE SKIN

This skin needs to be treated with great care as it is very easily irritated and often has a tendency to blotching, redness and rashes. It may develop fine broken veins across the cheeks and nose and also premature wrinkles. The use of any product on sensitive skin should be approached with caution and it is best to avoid Essential Oils and any but the plainest ingredients on very sensitive skin. If in any doubt seek professional or medical guidance on what to use.

What to use

Simple aids MILK • OATMEAL

Vegetable/Nut and other Oils APRICOT • JOJOBA • OLIVE

WRINKLES

See Mature skin.

Index